All the children were at school.
Mr Belter talked to the children.

1

The children looked at Mr Belter,
but Kevin looked out of the window.

'Look at the painting,' said Mr Belter.
'It is a painting of the Duke of Wellington.'
The children looked at the painting,
but Kevin looked out of the window.

Mr Belter looked at Kevin,
but Kevin looked out of the window.
'Kevin,' said Mr Belter.
'Look at the painting.
Who is it?'

Kevin looked at the painting.
'Is it Mr Keeping?' said Kevin.
'No, it is not!' said Mr Belter.

'We are going to paint,' said Mr Belter.
'What could we paint?'

'I could paint a dog,' said Jamila.
'I could paint a dog too,' said Rocky.
'I will paint Max.'

'I will paint a trampoline,' said Ben.
'We will paint the Duke of Wellington,'
said Tessa and Tony.
Kevin looked out of the window.

8

Mr Belter went over to Kevin.
Mr Belter was cross.
'You are going to paint too,' said the teacher.

Kevin grabbed some paint.
Splash!
Some of his paint
splashed over Rocky and Jamila.

Kevin went to get some water.
Splash!
Some of his paint went on Tony and Tessa.

'Look at my painting,' said Kevin.
Some of his paint went on Ben.

Kevin said to his mother,
'We did painting at school.'

'Jamila and Rocky were painting dogs,'
said Kevin.
'Ben was painting a trampoline
and Tony and Tessa were painting the
Duke of Wellington.'

'But what were you painting?' said his mother.

'I was painting all my friends,' said Kevin.